Beanbag Balls

These super squishy balls are great for games in the garden or on the beach!

KT-498-514

From the Doodle Drawers:

- Three coloured balloons
- Dried lentils
- Funnel
- Scissors

1.

Ask an adult to cut the necks off your three balloons. Place a funnel inside the opening of your first balloon and pour in a cup of lentils. You want it full, but still squeezable.

2.

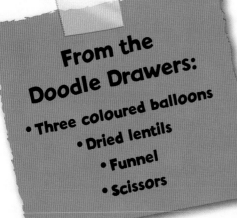

Take your second balloon and stretch it over the top of the first, covering the hole.

Do the same with the third balloon.

Ta-da! You have a brilliant ball to play with. Why not make two more and try your hand at juggling?

Paper Bag Puppets

Rainy day? Stay inside and make some crazy characters with our nifty puppet project!

From the Doodle Drawers:

- **Paper party bags**
- **Safety scissors**
- **Craft glue**
- **Coloured pens**
- **Crayons**
- **Paint**
- **Buttons, gems, ribbons and beads**

1.

Lay a paper bag flat with the folded bottom part facing up. This flap will be the face of your puppet and you can decorate it any way you like! We're making a little girl puppet.

Turn to the sticker page in this book and choose some eyes for your puppet. Stick them onto the flap.

2.

Create a mouth with coloured paper, pens or crayons. Put a circle under the flap, then add the upper lips to the flap edge. There are also mouth stickers in this book.

3.

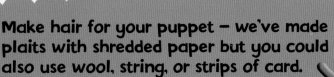

Make hair for your puppet – we've made plaits with shredded paper but you could also use wool, string, or strips of card.

4

Mister Maker™

Holiday Fun!
Craft Activity Book

Hello everyone, I'm Mister Maker!

In this book, I'll show you great
crafts to make and lots of art
fun to do on your holidays –
at home or away.
You'll never have a dull
day or boring trip again!

So, what are you waiting for?
Grab your glue stick and
let's make it!

Use the stickers
to decorate your
crafty projects!

Before You Start

You'll need to gather your art materials. Make sure you have the following basics . . .

- Safety scissors
- Craft glue
- Acrylic paint and brushes
- Pens, pencils and crayons
- A ruler
- Sticky tape

. . . then start collecting other interesting bits and pieces, so you can build your very own Doodle Drawers! Look out for:

- Coloured paper and card
- Sequins, buttons and beads
- Patterned paper
- Ribbons
- Glitter
- Stickers and labels

Each craft includes a few special signs with the instructions. Here's what each one means:

This means be careful with scissors, because they're sharp.

This means you'll need some help from an adult.

This means you can use your stickers in the craft.

4.

Now, create an outfit for your puppet. Stick paper or fabric to the front of the bag to create some cool clothes. Add collars and buttons.

5.

Cut out more coloured paper or use your pens and crayons to add other details like freckles, eyelashes and glasses.

6.

Use any other bits and bobs you find to add details – sticky gems, ribbons and beads all work well.

Now put your hand inside the paper bag and bring your puppet to life!

Puppet Performance

Create a whole cast of puppets with your friends and put on a show! There are all kinds of crazy characters you could craft.

Make a puppet theatre by hanging a sheet on a clothesline and standing behind it to hide your body – or you could just crouch behind the sofa. Now create different voices for your paper people and act out your stories!

Bottle Bowling Pins

Want to play outside today? Start collecting plastic bottles to make a rocking set of skittles!

From the Doodle Drawers:

- 10 plastic bottles
- Funnel
- Play sand or dried rice
- Paints
- Craft glue

Wash out the plastic bottles and let them dry completely.

Using a funnel, pour about 3 inches of play sand or dried rice into each bottle. This gives weight to the bowling pin.

1.

2.

Put some glue onto the top of the bottles and screw the lids back on. Leave them to dry until the bottles are glued shut.

3.

Decorate them! You may want to paint coloured patterns on your bottles, or cover them with your cool stickers. Or you might try a group of people or animals. We're making a huddle of penguins!

When the paint is dry, your set of pins is complete.

Ten-pin-tastic

Get bowling! Gather a group of friends and choose a safe place to play outside, like your garden, or ask an adult to take you to the park. Make a Beanbag Ball (page 3) and set the pins up in a triangle shape. Take it in turns to roll the ball at the skittles and keep score of how many you knock over each time. The person with the highest score at the end is the winner. Strike!

Souvenir Suitcase

Make your own special suitcase to store
your holiday mementoes!

1.

Carefully cover the lid and base of a
shoebox with brown wrapping paper.

From the Doodle Drawers:

- **Shoebox**
- **Glue**
- **Brown packing paper**
- **Safety scissors**
- **Duct tape**
- **White paper**
- **Crayons and coloured pens**
- **Old magazines and postcards**
- **Ribbon**
- **String**

2.

Use duct tape to attach the lid to
one edge of the box on the inside,
so it opens like a suitcase.

3.

Gather together pictures to glue onto
your suitcase.

Cut out photos of holiday places and maps
from magazines, and collect old postcards of
places you or your friends have been to.

You could design your own travel stickers by
cutting out shapes from white paper and
writing names of countries or funny parcel
labels, such as 'fragile' and 'this side up'.

And don't forget there are also special
travel stickers to use inside this book!

4.

Stick your labels all over the suitcase in different directions. You can glue them on top of each other and wrap them around corners and over edges.

5.

Make a handle. Ask an adult to poke two holes into the open edge of the box. Cut a ribbon and thread both ends through the holes, then tie them together on the inside.

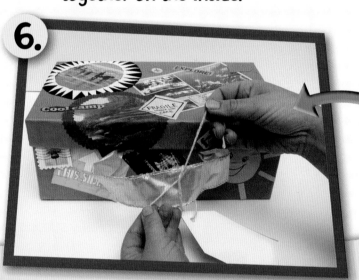

6.

Attach a luggage label. Cut it out of plain card, tie to your handle and write your name on it.

Collect and Keep!

You're ready to fill your suitcase! Collect objects from your holidays and put them in your keepsake box when you get home. You could store seashells, photographs, a bottle of sand, postcards and souvenirs. It will be a lovely reminder of the places you've been and people you've met!

MY HOLIDAY

Super Stamps

These simple stamps are great for
printing your own postcards!

**From the
Doodle Drawers:**
* Sponge
* Safety scissors
* Black marker pen
* Craft glue
* Small bottle or jar

1.

Place a small jar on a piece of
sponge and draw around the lid
with a black marker pen.

2.

Decide the shape you want your
stamp to be and draw the outline
onto your sponge, inside
the circle.

Ask an adult to cut out the shape.

3.

Stick the sponge onto the lid of
your bottle or jar. When it's dry,
you're ready to stamp!

Decorate a piece of card by dipping
your stamp into acrylic paint and
printing your shape onto it.
Cut them into postcards and send
them to your friends on holiday!

Sticky Picture Box

This box is made for travelling – and you can make different pictures again and again!

1.

Cut a piece of white felt to fit inside your box lid and glue it in place.

From the Doodle Drawers:
- Coloured felt
- Small plastic lunchbox
- Safety scissors
- Craft glue

2.

Cut out shapes from your coloured felt. Make circles, squares, flowers, leaves and any other shapes you like.

3.

Now make a picture! Felt sticks to felt really well, so simply place your shapes onto the white felt lid. Then peel them off and start again!

Store your shapes inside the box and take it with you – it's great for car journeys and aeroplane flights!

Funny Face Flip Book

Long plane journey ahead? Keep your fingers busy with this neat drawing project.

1.

Cut five pieces of white A4 paper into quarters.

From the Doodle Drawers:

• A4 white paper
• Safety scissors
• Black pen
• Empty jar or mug
• Pencil
• Coloured pens, pencils or crayons
• Stapler

2.

On each piece of paper, draw around the top of an empty jar or mug with a black pen, so you have a circle on each one.

Cut a strip of card about 2 centimetres wide and lay this through the centre of each circle. Draw two lines with a pencil, along the top and bottom of the strip, so you divide each circle into three sections.

3.

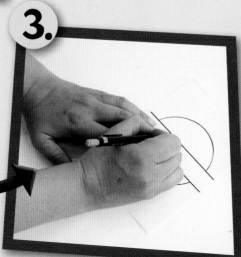

4.

Draw some funny faces! Make sure the eyes are in the top section of each circle, the nose in the middle, and the mouth at the bottom. Use plenty of colour and add details like earrings, hair, hats and beards. There are stickers in this book you can add too!

Once you've drawn all your faces, neatly stack your pages and ask an adult to staple them together.

5.

6.

Ask an adult to carefully cut along the two pencil lines, stopping before the edge where the pages are stapled together. Now flip away! When you flick through different sections, you'll see some crazy face combinations!

If you're going on a journey, ask an adult to prepare a blank stapled book before you leave, so you only need to bring your colouring things to make more crazy face combinations!

Ice Cream Sundae

Cool off on summer days at home, with this fab fake treat!

From the Doodle Drawers:

- Paper cup
- Paint
- Newspaper
- Large bowl
- Flour
- Salt
- Beads
- Craft glue
- Mini pompoms

1.

Paint a paper cup brown and then paint criss-crossed lines in white paint over the top, to look like an ice cream cone. Leave it to dry.

2.

Crumple some pieces of newspaper and stuff these inside the cup until it's 3/4 full.

3.

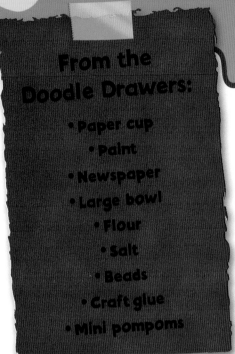

Now make your salt dough! In a large bowl, mix two cups of flour and one cup of salt, then add 1/2 cup of water.

4.

Push and knead the dough until it is firm, but still easy to shape. Add more water if you need to.

5.

Decide on three flavours of ice cream you'd like to make. Split the dough into three pieces and add paint to each of them. We've used pink for strawberry, green for mint and yellow for lemon!

6.

Roll two colours of dough into balls and place them in your cone, one on top of the other.

7.

Roll your final colour into a long sausage shape, then lay this on top of the ice cream in a spiral. It's just like whipped cream!

8.

Now decorate your sundae. Press beads into the dough to look like sprinkles and make some fake syrup by mixing paint with glue, then dribbling it over the top of your ice cream.
We've made strawberry syrup!

9.

Sharpen a brown crayon and use the shavings as chocolate flakes. Lastly, put a red pompom on top for a cherry!

More Food Fun!

Salt dough dries hard on its own, so leave your sculpture for a few days and it will set solid! Wrap any leftover salt dough in foil and keep it in the refrigerator for other projects. Why not try making more fake food, like eggs and sausages, a pizza or cupcakes!

This might look good enough to eat, but remember: it's only pretend ice cream, so don't put it in your mouth!

Little Creature Doodles

From the Doodle Drawers:

- **White paper**
- **Felt tip pens**
- **Thin black marker**

1.

Using felt tip pens, draw big dots onto a piece of white paper. These will form the body parts of your creatures.

2.

Take your thin black pen and bring your little friends to life! Think of all the animals you could draw: mice, dogs, cats, horses, lions, birds, bears – any creature should work. Add details like noses, mouths, ears, wings, legs and tails.

When you've filled your page, start another one! You could stick it onto some thicker paper to make a great gift card!

Happy Birthday

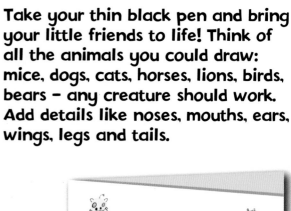